Developing Hi‖‖‖‖‖‖‖

C000022671

UNDERSTANDING AND INTERPRETING ...

Ages

10-11

Jane Shuter

A & C BLACK

Contents

Published 2007 by A & C Black Publishers Limited
38 Soho Square, London W1D 3HB
www.acblack.com

ISBN 978-0-7136-8391-2

Copyright text and illustrations © Bender Richardson White
Copyright cover illustration © Sholto Walker
Copyright photos pages 12 and 55 © TopFoto/Fotomas
Project managers: Lionel Bender and Ben White
Editors: Lucy Poddington and Deborah Kespert
Design: Susan McIntyre
Illustrator: David Benham
The publishers would like to thank Rick Weights and Alf Wilkinson of the Historical Association for their assistance in producing this series of books.

A CIP catalogue record for this book is available from the British Library.

Printed in Great Britain by Martins the Printers, Berwick on Tweed.

This book is produced using paper that is made from wood grown in managed, sustainable forests. It is natural, renewable and recyclable. The logging and manufacturing processes conform to the environmental regulations of the country of origin.

Introduction

Developing History is a series of seven photocopiable activity books for history lessons. Each book provides a range of activities that not only develop children's knowledge and understanding of events, people and changes in the past, but also provide opportunities to develop their investigative and interpretive skills.

The activities vary in their approach. Some are based on first-hand observations, some present text and images for the children to analyse, and others require the children to find information from books and electronic sources. They focus on questioning, observing, generating thoughts and ideas, planning, carrying out investigations, recording findings, checking and questioning findings and presenting explanations. The activities include independent and group work.

The activities in **Ages 10–11** are based on the QCA schemes of work for history at Key Stage 2 and support children's development in the following areas from the programme of study:

- Place events, people and changes into the correct period of time
- Use dates and vocabulary relating to the passing of time
- Understand the characteristic features of periods and societies studied, including ideas, beliefs, attitudes and experiences of men, women and children
- Social, cultural, religious and ethnic diversity of societies
- Reasons for, and results of, historical events, situations and changes
- Links between main events, situations and changes
- Recognise and give reasons for different representations and interpretations of the past
- Find out about events, people and changes from a range of sources of information, including ICT-based sources
- Ask and answer questions and select and record information relevant to the focus of the enquiry
- Recall, select and organise historical information
- Use dates and historical vocabulary to describe periods studied
- Communicate knowledge and understanding in a variety of ways.

The activities are linked with other areas of the curriculum where appropriate.

Each activity specifies the learning outcome and features a **Teachers' note** at the foot of the page, which may be masked before photocopying. This will flag any resources needed for the activity. Expanded teaching notes are also provided in the **Notes on the activities** on pages 5–11. This section gives further information and provides key vocabulary to work through at the start of each activity.

Most of the activity sheets end with a challenge (**Now try this!**) which reinforces and extends the children's learning and provides the teacher with an opportunity for assessment. These activities might be appropriate for only a few children; it is not expected that the whole class should complete them.

Organisation and resources

Most activities require few resources beyond pencils and general classroom items, including spare paper on occasion. However, because the programme of study for history requires the use of primary source materials and the examination of objects from the time being studied (not just drawings of these objects), there will be times when children will need additional resources. They may need to have access to books, CD-ROMs, DVDs or to computers to search the Internet for images and information. These occasions will be pointed out in the **Teachers' note**. You may want to use electronic interactive whiteboards or overhead projectors to display activity sheets or source material.

Ensure you have a simple class timeline to help the children place the period in its chronological context. The timeline helps them to meet the requirements to place events, people and changes into the correct periods of time and to use dates and vocabulary related to the passing of time. Clearly mark the direction in which to move along the timeline. The timeline needs to have AD and BC (and the direction in which these move along the timeline) clearly marked. It would also be useful to have a chart on the wall that shows how pre-decimal coinage worked. You will find it helpful to build up your own resource bank of books (including picture books and story books about the various study units), posters, newspapers and old photographs, especially of your local area or historic sites you and your class have visited.

Structure of a history lesson

To get the best use of the activity sheets, gather all the resources you need before the lesson. Spend 10 to 15 minutes discussing the activity and making sure all the children understand what they have to do and how they will achieve it. Give the children about 20 minutes on the activity. Allow 5 to 10 minutes for whole-class review and consolidation.\

Useful websites

You can find information and pictures relating to the topics in this book on the following websites:
www.barnardos.org.uk
www.victorianweb.org (This site is more useful for your research than for the children, but it has a wealth of information)
www.learningcurve.gov.uk
www.makingthemodernworld.org.uk/stories/the_age_of_the_engineer
www.primaryresources.co.uk/history
www.spartacus.schoolnet.co.uk

Further useful online resources are given in the **Notes on the activities** on pages 5–11.

The notes below expand upon those provided at the foot of the activity pages. They give ideas for making the most of the activity sheet, including suggestions for the whole-class introduction and discussion or for follow-up work. To help teachers to select appropriate learning experiences for their pupils, the activities are grouped into sections within each book, but the pages need not be presented in the order in which they appear unless stated otherwise.

What was it like living in Victorian Britain?

Resources

- For timeline work at the start of the unit: pictures of Queen Victoria in 1838 and 1897 (examples can be found at www.wga.hu/frames-e.html?/html/s/sully/victoria.html and www.thamesweb.co.uk/windsor/windsorhistory/images/victoria1897.jpg
- **Making a difference:** books, CD-ROMs or Internet access to research the life of Lord Shaftesbury; examples of obituaries from newspapers.

Rich and poor (page 12) encourages children to consider how different life was for children in Victorian Britain, depending on their age, sex and (most importantly) social class. To begin the lesson, remind the children about class in Victorian Britain by brainstorming some of the differences between the classes on the board. Stress that 'working class' was a label often attached to poor people who had no work. Discuss how those without work might think they would be more likely to find work in big cities and how children who were either orphans or left home for various reasons could end up on the streets of London. This provides a chance to make links with both citizenship and English (the story of Dick Whittington). Remind the children that primary sources come from the period they are studying, while secondary sources come from a later period. Say they will be looking at two primary sources in the activity.

> **Vocabulary:** source, primary, secondary, lass, upper class, middle class, working class, orphan.

Making a difference (page 13) encourages children to do their own research. You may wish to give them a general introduction to who Lord Shaftesbury was before you begin the activity. Shaftesbury contributed to so many areas of reform that you may wish to divide the class into four groups to consider the main reforms that had an effect on children: chimney sweeps, ragged schools, working conditions in mines and working conditions in factories. The groups could then report back and the information could be collated on the board for everyone to use in their obituaries. This is probably the best approach if the children have had limited opportunities for research previously. On the other hand, if they are more practised, you may feel that it is too restricting to limit them to one aspect of his life. This activity links with work in literacy.

> **Vocabulary:** obituary, reform, law, Act of Parliament, commission, enquiry.

Out to work (page 14). Before the children start the activity, explain that the laws came after many government enquiries into the working conditions of children and the effects on their health. Remind them that in many poor families the only people working were the children because employers preferred them – they paid children less than men or women. Tell the children there were three separate areas of work that were changed in the legislation: starting age, number of hours worked and working at night. Brainstorm arguments against setting specific targets for these on the board before beginning the activity. (Reasons for could include: no targets mean no regulation; some ages are too young to work etc. Reasons against could include: some children much bigger, stronger than others; how can employers know how old children are etc). This links to citizenship.

> **Vocabulary:** reform, law, Act of Parliament, factory, inspector, fine, deterrent.

School days (page 15). Before starting the activity, remind the children of what they have learned about changing attitudes to children and work. Say that this is linked to changing attitudes about school and that there were several laws passed about educating children in Victorian times. If they have done work on the Education Acts previously, remind them of the various requirements of the Acts. If not, say you will consider the Acts in detail later. After reading Charles Cooper's description of his school, the children could work out how many classes at their school would make 100 pupils and how easy it would be for them all to learn different things together in the school hall with one teacher and two helpers.

> **Vocabulary:** Education Act, compulsory, points of view.

Budget: 1 and 2 (pages 16–17) is a two-page activity, with a resource sheet and an activity sheet. The resource sheet gives the weekly budget for a working-class and a middle-class family. As an extension, children could discuss the 'extras' of the Fenners – including medical bills. In Victorian times, people had to pay for a doctor to visit and for medicine. Discuss what the Slacks would do if someone was sick. An alternative extension would be to link with PSHE healthy-eating points and discuss the fruit- and vegetable-eating of both families.

> **Vocabulary:** class, upper class, middle class, working class, servant, budget.

Finding a builder (page 18) encourages children to think about the resources that Victorian people had available to find particular tradespeople. Before starting the activity, brainstorm all the ways that people might find a plumber to mend a leak today. Once you have a list, work through it crossing out resources that the Victorians did not have (Internet search etc). Add street directories to the remaining resources and explain that they were a Victorian version of Yellow Pages. Also discuss the fact that asking locally was more likely to get results: there were many more small local businesses.

> **Vocabulary:** street directory, milkman.

Cleaning up cities (page 19) encourages children to think about the fact that people, in the past and now, can have different views on the same situation. Before beginning the activity, read the children the poem *Mr Nobody*, which can be found at website www.poetryfoundation.org/archive/poem.html?id=171645. Discuss who Mr Nobody is, and why he is useful. Explain that his poem was a very popular poem at the time: both parents and children would have known it. Remind the children that this was a time when towns were growing rapidly and when parliament was beginning to debate whether or not to interfere in issues of public health.

> **Vocabulary:** *government, law, debate, parliament, cholera, hygiene, commission, enquiry.*

How did life in our locality change in Victorian times?

Resources

- This unit focuses on local history. The resources offered by record offices and local libraries vary widely. Consult the local record office (or your History advisor) about the kinds of material available in your area and the easiest way to access it. It would be very useful to have photos on display of both the town and countryside in your area: showing homes, industry, transport, schools and public buildings. They can then be referred to in discussions for several of the activities.
- **Census records: 1 and 2:** data for a street in your local area if you choose to extend the activity
- **Planning a school:** a Victorian board school plan from your local area
- **On the move:** a map of part of your local town, showing transport links (rail, canal, tram road). Possibly photos of Victorian transport (see notes)
- **Home sweet home:** examples of estate agents' property brochures.

Census records: 1 and 2: (pages 20–21) is a two-sheet activity. You may prefer to do the activity as a whole-class session. This activity could be extended by moving on to look at the census records for a local street. You can choose to provide the children with copies of the pages or with transcripts of the pages (some census recorders had handwriting that is easy to read; others are more of a challenge!) depending on your assessment of what best suits the children. The activity could be extended by use of street and trade directory entries for the same street for a variety of years, depending on the time available. Alternatively, you could extend it into a discussion of families then and now, for a PSHE link.

> **Vocabulary:** *census return, household, occupation.*

Planning a school (page 22) encourages the children to study plans of buildings carefully and relate them to each other and to their own school. The activity could be done as a whole-class activity, depending on how much experience the children have had of this type of activity. Begin by telling the children that these plans are both simplified plans of Victorian schools – one in a village, the other in a town. This activity could be extended by drawing a plan of your school on the board with you doing the drawing as the children discuss what goes where.

> **Vocabulary:** *classroom, school house.*

On the move (page 23) helps children to think about the various types of transport available in Victorian times. You could support this activity by displaying photos of Victorian transport types on the walls (photos of crowded streets in your area are likely to show a variety of transport).

> **Vocabulary:** *canal, barge, cart.*

Home sweet home (page 24) is designed to be used following a whole-class discussion of the features of Victorian buildings. Begin the lesson by using photos of your local area that show sash windows, bargeboards, loft windows, bay window, porch over door, iron railings. They need to work with local buildings to meet the requirement for the Unit. Make sure the children are confident with the terms before they begin the activity. The activity could be replaced/extended by a trip to a local street that has Victorian houses.

> **Vocabulary:** *sash window, brickwork, Gothic, bargeboard, dormer window.*

How has life in Britain changed since 1948?

Resources

- **Looking good:** a display of images of clothes, 1940s to modern day (not required for the activity, but useful as a discussion prompt).

Staying in (page 25). Begin the activity by discussing the idea of having to stay in, for example on a wet day. Brainstorm the ways in which the children could entertain themselves and list these on the board. Make sure the list includes TV, radio, ipods, cards, books, comics, board games and dominoes. Then explain that children in previous decades had less choice and that some of the things that they entertained themselves with are not often used now.

> **Vocabulary:** *decade, entertainment, invent, board game, cards.*

Looking good (page 26). Introduce the activity by discussing how fashion, because of the way it changes so often, is a very good reflection of the times. Tell the children that they are going to look at the years since the 1940s by looking at one fashion item: the dress. The activity could be extended by a similar look at an item of men's clothing, such as the suit, using colour pictures of suits from various decades. A further extension would be to look at fashion through family photos that the children bring in. As a plenary, date the clothing on the board and discuss what the clothes had to say about the person who wore them, for example the miniskirt is very short and fashionable – only a young woman would wear it.

> **Vocabulary:** *decade, utility clothing, miniskirt, power-suit.*

Getting the news (page 27) helps children to understand how ways of communicating have changed since the 1940s. Introduce the activity by saying that technology is always changing and new developments change our lives in many ways. You could collect examples of this on the board from planes to computers to mobile phones. You could extend the activity by discussing how changes to the way people keep in touch affect how they behave. Do people plan ahead less carefully? How quickly do they want replies to messages sent, for example, by email?

> **Vocabulary:** *decade, communication, news, media, technology.*

Different schools (page 28) encourages the children to focus on the difference between fact and opinion in what they are told. Depending on how much previous work they have done on this, you might want to begin by telling them about an event – personal or historical, using both fact and opinion and then unpicking that event with them in class discussion, listing the facts and the opinions on the board. The activity could be extended by asking the children what might cause the different reactions of the other people who were in Sheila's class. This leads to thinking about the question: 'Does the fact that different people have different reactions to (and opinions about) the same experience mean that these reactions and opinions are no use to a historian?'

> **Vocabulary:** *fact, opinion, reaction, blackboard.*

Memories (page 29) involves the children in conducting an interview at home before a class discussion of what they found out. The point of the interviews is not so much the information they collect as the realisation that memories provide historical information and are better at providing some sorts of information than other sorts. When giving out the activity sheets, brainstorm the kinds of questions they might choose to ask. Be sure to collect at least 10, preferably more, on the board, so there is a reasonable amount for them to choose from. The activity could be adapted by choosing a set of questions in class and then compiling data charts using the information. Once the data has been collected, discuss with the children what they found out: what did the interviewees enjoy talking about most; what kind of information were they best at providing? Collate this information on the board under the headings 'Memories are best at …' 'Memories are worst at …'

> **Vocabulary:** *interview, interviewer, interviewee.*

Cause and effect (page 30). Cause and effect helps the children to consider how a change in one aspect of life can have a knock-on effect on other areas of life. Introduce this idea of causal links by discussing the effect of only being able to shop within walking distance. People would need to think carefully about when they shopped (the weather would be a big factor). Discuss that now we have cars and Internet shopping to remove many of these problems.

> **Vocabulary:** *wages, goods, factories, causal links.*

Choosing sources (page 31) is a useful activity to wind up the unit. It also gives children a chance to show they understand the primary/secondary source distinction. Begin by discussing your main project with the class and making a list on the board of the various kinds of sources of evidence that they were able to use for each decade. Warn them that while these sources were useful for their main project, they might be too specific to be useful for another. So photographs are very useful whereas population statistics would not be useful for a project on music (but other statistics, such as record sales information, might).

> **Vocabulary:** *source, primary, secondary, evidence.*

Who were the ancient Greeks?

Resources
- Timeline and mapwork to start the unit
- Map to show ancient Greece and the city states. An online map of these can be found at www.bartleby.com/67/aeolia01.html
- **Olympic Games:** for **Now try this!** the children will need a clear image of at least one Greek vase with an Olympic event on it. There are many such images in books. To find images on the web that do not offend the sensibilities with nudity, go to Bridgeman Art Library website www.bridgeman.co.uk and search for charioteers [BAL 28560 or CZA 228737], boxers [BAT 99068], footracers [DTR 114497 or XIR 158663] and discus and javelin throwers [BAL 110798].

Before beginning the unit, spend a lesson locating ancient Greece in time and space. Mark the period 800–323 BC on the timeline. Remind the children about BC and AD dating, and how BC dating works backwards, increasing the further back in time you go. Look at a relief map of Greece and, if possible, some photographs that show how much of Greece is broken up by mountains and the sea. Discuss how this would affect getting around, working together etc. Explain that this is why city states grew up, based on a city and the farmlands around it. Look at a city states map. Count them and discuss their size.

Democracy (page 32) encourages children to consider Athenian democracy. Discuss with the children how monarchies, oligarchies and democracies are run. Discuss who can vote in the version of democracy used in the UK. Why are some people living in this country not allowed to vote? Why might this be seen as fair? This discussion will link to citizenship and will get the children thinking about the issues that they will meet in the activity. The **Now try this!** is an empathy activity. The children may feel it is clearly not fair that women do not vote, but they need to put themselves in the place of Greek women, who were not expected to take part in almost any activity outside the home – even the shopping! This would give the women a different outlook on voting rights.

> **Vocabulary:** *democracy, city state, citizen, government, monarchy, oligarchy, slave, vote.*

Don't anger the gods (page 33) gives the children a chance to consider the beliefs of the ancient Greeks while examining a particular Greek legend. You may want to read and discuss the story as a whole-class activity before beginning the activity sheet. It links to Literacy work.

> **Vocabulary:** *god, goddess, beliefs.*

The Battle of Salamis: 1 and 2 (pages 34–35). This activity has two sheets: an information sheet and an activity sheet. The focus of the activity is using different sources of information to build up a picture and considering the impartiality of a source. The children use the sources to find out about Greek warfare but they need to think about them as sources as well. Depending on the amount of previous work the children have done on sources and their reliabiliy you may want to do this activity as a whole-class exercise.

> **Vocabulary:** *source, primary, secondary, bias, impression, fleet, Persians.*

The Olympic Games: 1 and 2 (pages 36–37) encourages children to see that they can make inferences from sources, as well as take information from them. Discuss this with the children before they begin the exercise. Use this passage, describing the event called pankration, as an example: 'Arrachion's opponent held him with his legs in a scissor grip. At the same time, he began to strangle him. Arrachion, who had hold of his opponent's feet, broke one of his toes. Arrachion died from the strangling. But the referees noticed that, just before he died, his opponent had given in because of the pain in the broken toe. So Arrachion was proclaimed the winner.' This source tells you that pankration was a contest between two men. It was a violent event, which seemed to have few rules. There were referees who were watching closely. However, these referees did not seem to feel they should stop strangling or toe-breaking. You can also deduce that fairness was so important that the referees made the dead man the winner, rather than the person who was still alive.

> **Vocabulary:** *source, chariot, turning post.*

A Greek theatre (page 38) encourages the children to consider a historical building as a piece of evidence. Begin by discussing Greek buildings generally. Remind the children that ordinary homes (even of the very wealthy) were not made from stone: only public buildings were. Tell them the diagram on the sheet has been drawn up from archaeological evidence. The activity could be extended by a general class discussion of buildings as sources and what they cannot tell us. Stress that what they can tell us is useful but, like all evidence, they have their limitations. They can tell us plays were often performed at religious festivals, when sacrifices were made (on the altar) and music was played (in the orchestra and chorus area). The chorus sang, danced and told the stories, which were either comedies or tragedies. The actors played out the story and spoke their lines. The buildings cannot tell us about the people who became actors, how many actors and orchestra players there were, nor can they tell us about the sex, age or class of the audience.

> **Vocabulary:** *orchestra, altar, stage, sacrifice.*

How do we use ancient Greek ideas today?

Resources
- **Wordy Greeks:** dictionaries or access to Internet so children can access a prefix/suffix site at www.infoplease.com/ipa/A0907013.html

Wordy Greeks (page 39). Before starting the activity, remind the children how long ago the ancient Greeks lived. Ask them if they think the ancient Greek language has survived at all today. Explain that modern Greek is similar, but different, and that ancient Greek is alive in English, too. The activity could be extended by collecting everyone's words on the board and having a whole-class quickfire session to fill the gaps. This activity links with Literacy.

> **Vocabulary:** *alphabet, language, prefix, suffix.*

Perfect proportion (page 40) helps the children to understand the importance of ratio to Greek builders. Stress that ratios are about the relationship between two numbers and that the numbers themselves are not important. You may want to do some whole-class work with simple ratios on the board, until you feel they are confident with the concept. In the second part of the activity, help the children to measure the diagram with a ruler and find three pairs of measurements that have a ratio of 9:4. For example, the comparative length of the large inner chamber compared to the small inner chamber is 9:4, and the relative length and breadth of the large inner chamber is also 9:4. Depending on the amount of work they have done in this area and how confident you feel they are, this could be done as a whole-class activity. Even when children have no experience at all, they quickly get the hang of it in a teacher-led discussion.

> **Vocabulary:** *ratio, proportion, symmetrical, fact, opinion.*

Hippocrates (page 41) introduces the children to the ideas of Hippocrates (who lived between about 460 and 370 BC). Tell them he is called the 'father of medicine' and explain that he was the first doctor that we know of to believe that all illness had a cause that was not magical. His idea of observation, prediction then treatment is the way doctors still work today. The activity could be extended by a research project on Asclepius, the ancient Greek god of medicine and health. Find out what went on in an asclepieion. Which kind of ancient Greek doctor would the children rather visit?

> **Vocabulary:** *patient treatment, observation, symptoms.*

Olympic guidebook: 1 and 2 (pages 42–43) is a two-sheet activity. It encourages the children to discover similarities and differences between modern and ancient Olympics and to produce a 'guidebook' for a modern child time-travelling back to the ancient Olympics. You could adapt/extend the activity by having the children work in groups to prepare a report from a returning time traveller on one aspect of the ancient Olympics (what sports there were/who competed/ facilities) saying what they saw, what went right/wrong etc. A representative from each group could then give the report to the class.

> **Vocabulary:** *religious festival, professional, amateur.*

How can we find out about the Indus Valley civilisation?

Resources
- **Timeline:** begin this unit by working with the timeline, finding the dates for the Indus Valley civilisation (3500–2500 BC: stress that these dates are approximate) and fixing them on the timeline, reminding the children about AD and BC dating as you do so. A map that shows the area settled by the Indus Valley people would be a useful asset on the wall throughout the study of the unit.
- **Archaeological evidence:** a photograph of the Great Bath www.mohenjodaro.net/greatbath25.html
- **Interpreting the evidence:** photographs of Indus Valley artefacts. These can be found in reference books, on relevant CD-ROMs and on the Internet: try www.harappa.com or you

could go to www.bbc.co.uk/schools/indusvalley/ and follow the links to the Museum. The BBC site is for younger children and the artefacts have captions that provide some of the information the children are expected to deduce.

Similar cities (page 44). Begin the lesson by asking the children how an archaeologist from the future might find out about our civilisation. Collect answers on the board. There will probably be a large number of written types of evidence. Explain that we cannot read the Indus Valley writing, so we have to rely on working things out from the artefacts (large and small) they have left behind. Their cities are very large artefacts. Tell the children that the simplified plans are based on as much of these cities as have been excavated and that none of them has been entirely excavated. The upper town areas were mostly public buildings and large houses. The lower town areas were full of workshops and small houses. Draw a distinction between the 'best guess' ideas of archaeologists using existing evidence and 'wild guess' guesses without evidence. This will set the children up for the next activity sheet.

> **Vocabulary:** *archaeologist, excavate, artefact, plan.*

Archaeological evidence (page 45) develops the 'best guess' ideas introduced at the end of the last activity. Remind the children of that discussion before they begin. You may wish to do this activity as groupwork or as a whole-class exercise. Once the children have worked out the purpose of the building, you could show them a picture of the Great Bath, for example at www.mohenjodaro.net/greatbath25.html. For the extension activity, make sure that the children work on the basis of some of the evidence, however wild their surmises. The activity links with literacy work.

> **Vocabulary:** *archaeologist, evidence, guesswork, fact, drain, waterproof, pressure.*

Interpreting evidence (page 46) gives the children practice at making deductions from artefacts from the period. Explain that, when it is not possible to visit a museum and see actual artefacts, photographs of the artefacts can be treated as a primary source. Go through the difference between a photo and a drawing of the same thing – relate this to photos and drawings of their home, family members and so on. Introduce the activity by telling the children they will be choosing one artefact to write about (explaining this to suit whatever resources you are providing). Tell them they will need to look at the artefact closely and think about it very carefully. Depending on their experience of working with artefacts, you could begin by producing a modern artefact and discussing what it tells us: thinking about what it is made from, who could have made it, who for, what it was used for, would it be expensive and so on. You could then move on to the Indus Valley artefact.

> **Vocabulary:** *artefact, evidence.*

Different views (page 47) introduces the children to the problem of studying a culture with an unknown language. Begin by displaying a short piece of writing (no more than two sentences) in a language that no one in the class speaks. Ask them if they know what it says. How will you find out? By, for example, using dictionaries or finding someone who speaks the language. But what if there is no one alive who speaks the language and no dictionaries? This is where we are with the Indus Valley script.

> **Vocabulary:** *symbol, translate, translation.*

How can we find out about the Aztecs?
Resources
- **Timeline:** begin this unit by working with the timeline, finding the dates for the Aztec civilisation (AD 1200–1520) and fixing them on the timeline, reminding the children about AD and BC dating as you do so. A map that shows the area controlled by the Aztecs would be a useful asset on the wall throughout the study of the unit.
- The activity sheet that uses photographs of artefacts in the Indus Valley section can be used here with Aztec artefacts.

Aztec society (page 48) introduces children to the Aztec social structure. Before they begin the activity discuss the idea of social structure and how society is run. They should be familiar with the concept by Year 6, and should be able to remember several different ways of running society, depending on their previous history studies. If you feel they need more than just a quick reminder, discuss why people need to organise themselves and have people in charge and doing different jobs. What are the benefits? What would happen otherwise? What are the problems? You could extend the activity with role-play, assigning one person in the class as the emperor and others for the other levels – with most people as workers/slaves. They have to work out what their duties and responsibilities are and what the benefits of their position are. Which people have the best balance of duties and benefits?

> **Vocabulary:** *society, emperor, noble, governor, priest, warrior, worker, merchant, slave, point of view.*

Solve Montezuma's problem (page 49) focuses on cause and effect. Because of the myth of Quetzalcoatl, the Aztecs did not immediately fight the Spanish. They welcomed them and seemed to want to help them and give them anything they wanted. Because they were welcomed in this way, the Spanish thought the Aztecs were not good warriors and were scared of the Spanish, their horses and their guns and cannons. This made them more likely to decide to conquer Aztec lands, rather than make a treaty with them. Introduce the activity with some discussion of cause and effect. The amount of time you spend on this will depend on how often the class has done similar work. If they need to do quite a lot of work, then try using contemporary, domestic examples to illustrate cause and effect, not historical ones. The activity could be extended to become a role-play debate of the issues involved.

> **Vocabulary:** *cause, effect, god, weapons.*

Reaching conclusions (page 50) helps children to understand different viewpoints. Begin the activity by reminding the children that different people have different perspectives on things. Emphasise that this is especially true in situations where one country takes over another country. You could remind the children, if they have studied the Victorians already, of how the

British felt that their building an empire was a good thing not just for Britain but also for the 'savages' or 'natives' that the empire 'civilised'. This was their point of view. However, the local people in the lands they took over would see things very differently. The activity could be extended/adapted to become a role-play debate of the issues involved, if not used on the previous sheet. Children could prepare for a courtroom trial against the Spanish for invading, with arguments for the prosecution/defence.

> **Vocabulary:** *opinion, fact, point of view, Spanish conquest, Catholic, slave, sacrifice.*

Take a closer look (page 51). Be sure to explain to the children that there is a big difference between a drawing that is based on evidence (or a careful drawing of an artefact) and wild, creative surmises or drawings that make an artefact 'prettier' and so on. Link this to the 'best guess' archaeology idea. Leave time to end the activity with a discussion of the children's deductions. Make sure that you discuss whether human sacrifice (or any kind of live sacrifice) means the Aztecs were cruel. Point out that they believed that the gods wanted human sacrifice and that, if they did not have it, the gods could bring all sorts of disasters on the Aztecs. If they did not please the gods they could be wiped out. So it does not necessarily mean they enjoyed killing.

> **Vocabulary:** *sacrifice, altar, temple, gods, artefact.*

What were the effects of Tudor exploration?

Resources

* **Timeline:** introduce the unit by working with the timeline, finding the dates of Tudor rule and fixing them on the timeline, reminding the children about AD and BC dating as you do so. While working with the timeline, tell the children that the Tudors sent explorers out to sea searching for new land and for sea routes to eastern countries where expensive silks and spices came from. The Spanish and Portuguese had found and settled in South America. They had found it rich in gold, silver and pearls. Treasure ships sailed back to Spain loaded with these things. So the Tudors looked north. Were there lands there that had similar treasures?

* A map that shows England, the Atlantic and Virginia would be useful. There are maps drawn by John White from the time that show the villages and islands mentioned. Remind the children that the settlers were moving between the mainland of Virginia and the islands. It will also be useful to have a larger map of Virginia that marks the following places: Croatoan, Roanoke, Hatarak, Secotan. A map from the time can be found at the official Roanoke site at www.nps.gov/fora/whitede.htm

Reasons for exploring: 1 and 2 (pages 52–53) encourages the children to think why people would want to face the dangers and discomforts of exploration. You will have already introduced some ideas in the work they did on the timeline. This activity extends this by focusing on Tudor exploration and settlement in North America. The activity could be extended by explaining that descriptions such as those in Sources A and B were often used both to recruit settlers and to encourage people to put money into the next trip: how might this affect their reliability?

> **Vocabulary:** *source, reliable, settle, settler.*

Cross the Atlantic (page 54) provides a race game to familiarise the children with the dangers of exploration. They will find that there are more dangers and problems than benefits! Depending on how much work they have done previously on exploration, you may need to explain that the explorers' navigation equipment depended on them making calculations from the sun, moon and stars. The activity could be extended by getting the children to think of extra problems that the travellers might face (keeping in period – dropping their mobile overboard doesn't count!). Alternatively, brainstorm the problems of going to settle in a new place where there is nothing – so they have to build their own homes, grow their food from seed having cleared land first and so on. They could then devise a game around these problems.

> **Vocabulary:** *rigging, crew, chart, navigate.*

The people of Virginia (page 55) encourages the children to think about how the indigenous people of Virginia were living before the English arrived. There should be time to collect the answers together on the board and consider a few supplementary questions: Do the people look peaceful and settled? Does the village look well organised? Does it look like part of a larger settlement? How far does the engraving agree with the impression given by Barlowe and Lane in the first activity? The people lived in organised communities: the village has a section with houses, straight paths, fenced areas of crops. They seem to have had ceremonies, which could have been religious – notice the group dancing in a line across the main path. They did not wear much clothing. All the houses were built in the same style.

> **Vocabulary:** *indigenous, settlement.*

Things go wrong (page 56) looks at why the Roanoke settlement failed. The debate could be a whole-class debate, in which case you should chair it to make sure all points are raised. It may be that some people who disagree with the majority say they will go/stay behind anyway. That is fine, but people who decide not to go back have to explain how they will survive. After the debate, tell the children what the settlers decided. They went home. Two weeks later, the supply ships came. The people who had come on these ships to join the settlement decided to go home, leaving 15 soldiers in the fort. By the time supply ships returned the following year, 14 of the soldiers were missing and one had been killed, probably by the local people.

> **Vocabulary:** *settlers, miners, fort, savages, vote.*

Lost: 1 and 2 (pages 57–58) underlines the fact that we cannot always find out what happened in the past – there is not enough evidence to be certain of some things and people have different theories. It also gives the children a chance to empathise with a person in a particular situation. Begin the activity by telling them that John White wrote a great deal about the 1586 and 1587 expeditions. He went on the 1585 expedition as an artist. He made many drawings and paintings that were published at the time. It was the nearest the Tudors could get to taking photos or film. The village drawing on page 55 is one of his. He was asked to go back in 1587 as governor of the new settlement. What happened then is a long story, but here is a short version of it. The activity could be extended by a discussion of the types of evidence the children would need to prove or disprove the theories.

> **Vocabulary:** *settler, settlement, expedition, fort, theory.*

Changing our lives (page 59) provides the children with a chance to consider the long-term impact of exploration. Introduce this activity by discussing how things that happened long ago are not just in a sealed bubble at some other point in time. What happens in the past shapes the future, including our present. Get the children thinking about the impact of Tudor exploration on our lives today. Brainstorm the effects of the Tudor settlement in America on our modern lives. If you consider it appropriate, the activity could be adapted/extended by a whole-class discussion of the question in the extension activity. It is important that the children understand that people in the past did not have access to the same range of information that we do. We have years of research to show that smoking is harmful. However, they did not. This does not mean they were wrong, or stupid.

> **Vocabulary:** *impact, tobacco, plantation.*

What can we learn about recent history from studying the life of a famous person?

Resources
- **Mary Quant:** Books, CD-ROMs and Internet access to research Mary Quant. A display of images of Mary Quant and her fashions would be useful.

Mary Quant (page 60) gives the children the opportunity to do some research. Mary Quant may connect with the children's project work for this unit, or not. The amount of time you spend introducing the unit will vary according to how much work the children have done on 1960s London, fashion and so on. Begin by saying this is a research project looking at the impact one person can make in society. You might like to discuss, generally, if the children think that one person can make a difference and bring about change. Collect examples of people they think might have done this (you can discuss this in terms of the whole world and all of history). The activity could be adapted so that different groups research different aspects of Mary Quant's life and report back. You could collate all the biographical information at the end of the lesson on a big version of the chart.

> **Vocabulary:** *society, profile, fashion, impact.*

The swinging sixties (page 61). Begin by reminding children that the Second World War ended in 1945, but the effects of the war (including rationing and shortages – even of food and clothes) went on into the 1950s. Remind the children about clothing rationing and utility clothing. Explain that before the war many women made all their own clothes. Tell them that until the mid-1950s there were clothes for women and girls and clothes for men and boys, but no clothes for 'teenagers' or even an idea of teenagers. A useful site to look at, with articles on the mini, the 1950s and utility clothing, is www.fashion-era.com/index.htm. The activity could be extended by a discussion about how different people might

have been affected by all the changes: a young woman living in London; a middle-aged man living in Scotland; a young woman living in Wales; a young man living in London; a baby born in Birmingham. There is no single 'right' answer to this debate, but it will make the children think about the effect of different circumstances.

> **Vocabulary:** *rationing, fashion.*

Making minis fashionable (page 62) introduces children to the idea that the criteria you apply to choosing 'the first …', 'the inventor of …' etc makes a big difference to who wins! There are usually three main points: who 'invented' it; who first made it famous; who made it affordable. This applies to all kinds of history. Edward Jenner is seen as the inventor of vaccination for smallpox. In fact, a doctor in the West Country had been doing the same thing to his patients for years, but had never told anyone about what he was doing, so had not spread the knowledge or the benefits. Begin by reminding the children of the difference between fact and opinion. Discuss the point that it is possible to have a wide range of valid opinions about the importance of something in history depending on your viewpoint and circumstances.

> **Vocabulary:** *mini, design, designer, invent, point of view.*

Fashion plus: 1 and 2 (pages 63–64) reinforces the idea that different people can have different opinions about events and their importance. Depending on how much experience the children have had of this, you may wish to begin the lesson by discussing it in a more familiar context before they begin the activity. People who are interested in fashion will be quick to look for connections that show that fashion was influential. Others, like Ivy Gross, will look for examples that show fashion was not important. You could extend the activity by discussing how the way you dress affects you and other people. Produce a wide range of photos of people in different clothes: a firefighter, a doctor, politicians in suits, clowns, rock stars, teenagers, etc and talk about how what they are wearing leads you to make assumptions about them. Does this support the idea of fashion as important, or not?

> **Vocabulary:** *opinion, fact, point of view, impact, miniskirt, campaign, nuclear weapons, fashion.*

Rich and poor

Understand that ways of life differed greatly across Victorian society

What can you tell about the boy in each source?
• Make notes in the table.

Source A

I spoke to a boy of about thirteen. He had no shirt, only a ragged jacket and trousers. He wore one old shoe too big for him tied on with string. He had a woman's boot on the other foot. He begged in the street, because he could not find work. He lived on leftover crusts of bread. He slept on the street or in half-built buildings.

From a book written by Henry Mayhew in 1849.

Source B

Engraving from 1850 of rich children saying goodnight to their parents.

	Source A	Source B
Food		
Clothes		
Bed		

• **Write a description like Mayhew's for the boy in the picture.**
• **Underline what you know for sure in blue.**
• **Underline what you have guessed in red.**

Teachers' note Before beginning the activity, remind the children about the Victorian class system and the distinction between primary and secondary sources. Primary sources come from the time they are studying, while secondary sources come from a later period. Tell them they will be looking at two primary sources.

Developing History
Ages 10–11
© A & C BLACK

Making a difference

Understand that the work of individuals can change an aspect of society

- **Plan an** obituary **for Lord Shaftesbury.**
- **Include the most important reforms he made.**
- **Use the word bank to help you.**

An obituary tells you about the life of a person who has died.

Born		Died	
Family			
Reforms	1. _____ _____ 2. _____ _____ 3. _____ _____ 4. _____ _____		

Now try this!

- **Write the obituary for a column in a newspaper.**
- **Design it on paper or using a computer.**

Teachers' note Begin the lesson by working through the words in the word bank and making sure all the children understand what they mean. The children should read obituaries from newspapers to help them complete the activity. Discuss the style in which obituaries are written. The children will need access to books, CD-ROMs or the Internet for research.

Developing History
Ages 10–11
© A & C BLACK

Out to work

Consider how attitudes to children changed over time

How do the laws about children working in factories show a change in attitudes to children?

- **Write your answer on the notepad.**

1833	Children under 9 years old cannot work.
	Children 9–13 can only work 9 hours a day.
	Children 13–16 can only work 12 hours a day.
	No one under 18 can work all night.
1844	Children can start work at 8 years old.
	Children 8–13 can only work 6.5 hours a day.
	Children under 18 cannot work over 12 hours a day.
1847	Children under 18 cannot work over 10 hours day or night.
1850	Children under 18 cannot work over 10.5 hours a day and not at night.
1867	Children under 18 cannot work more than 10 hours a day or night.

Now try this!

- **Write a newspaper report about children's working hours in 1867.**
- **Explain how the hours might affect a factory worker's family.**
- **How might they affect a doctor's family?**

Teachers' note Remind the children of what they have learned about children as sole wage earners in Victorian times. Point out that the laws changed to take account of different problems: sometimes the age of starting work went up to stop them working at night.

Developing History
Ages 10–11
© A & C BLACK

School days

In my school in 1877 one teacher and two pupil teachers taught a hundred boys and girls, aged six to twelve, in one big room. It cost 2s a week to go to school. Everyone walked to school, some as far as six miles each way. We learned to read, write and do maths. We also did some botany and geography. There were singing lessons and the girls did sewing in the afternoon.

Written by Charles Cooper in 1964, remembering his first school, which he went to in 1877.

- **Write four differences between this school in 1877 and your school today.**

- **Write two things that are the same.**

Differences	Similarities
1. _____	1. _____
2. _____	_____
3. _____	2. _____
4. _____	_____

The 1880 Education Act said children aged 5–10 had to go to school.

The 1891 Education Act said school was free for children aged 5–10.

- **Work with a partner.**

- **Discuss why it was important to have free education.**

  Why was it important for education to be compulsory?

How would a Victorian child describe your school?
- **Write a description from their point of view.**

Teachers' note Tell the children that the account on the page is a primary source: the person was at school in 1877. Remind the children about pre-decimal money and that 2s means two shillings.

Developing History
Ages 10–11
© A & C BLACK

Budget: 1

Understand that ways of life differed greatly across Victorian society

The Slack family: a working-class budget

In an interview in 1842, Edward Slack said that he and his wife knitted stockings. There were six daughters and a son in the family. They all knitted stockings, too. The most the family could earn in a week was 12 shillings. It was less if someone was ill, or when there was a new baby. This is how they spent their money:

The Slack family were not really poor because they were working. They were supposed to pay 8d a month to help the poor and 2d a month to help repair the roads. They almost never made these payments.

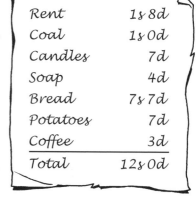

Rent	1s 8d
Coal	1s 0d
Candles	7d
Soap	4d
Bread	7s 7d
Potatoes	7d
Coffee	3d
Total	12s 0d

In old money:
12d (pence) = 1s (shilling)
20s (shillings) = £1 (pound).

The Fenner family: a middle-class budget

A book on how to run a home, published in the early 1840s, describes the budget of a professional man called Mr Fenner. He had a wife, three children and a maid to clean and help with the cooking. His income was £4 15s a week. This is how the Fenner family spent their money:

Rent	10s 0d	Cheese	1s 3d
Coal and wood	3s 9d	Milk	1s 6d
Candles + oil for lamps	1s 2d	Sugar	3s 0d
Soap	1s 2d	Spices, salt, pepper and	
Other cleaning stuff	9d	other grocery	3s 0d
Bread and flour	6s 0d	Meat	10s 6d
Vegetables and fruit	3s 0d	Fish	3s 6d
Tea	2s 6d	Beer, wine etc.	7s 0d
Butter	3s 6d	Total	£3 1s 7d

The family also paid £1 6s a month for the maid and £1 a month for school fees and other lessons for the children. They expected to spend about £3 a month on clothes and 12s for medical bills and entertainment.

Teachers' note Use this with the activity sheet on page 17. Before starting the activity, remind the children of Victorian class distinctions. Read through the budgets together – with a larger version on the board. Remind the children about old money (referring to a wall chart if you have one).

Developing History
Ages 10–11
© A & C BLACK

Budget: 2

- **Complete the questionnaire about how the two families on sheet 1 spent their money.**

1. What foods does the Slack family buy?

_____

2. What foods does the Fenner family buy that the Slacks don't buy?

_____

_____

3. What do the Slacks buy to drink?

_____

4. What do the Fenners buy to drink that the Slacks don't buy?

_____

5. Why do you think the Slacks buy the food and drink they do?

_____

_____

6. What do you think an upper-class family would buy to eat and drink?

_____

_____

What do the Fenners and Slacks use for heating and lighting?

- **Compare their spending on these items.**

Teachers' note Use this sheet together with the information sheet on page 16. The children could work in groups of five or six, appointing one member of the group to act as scribe and record the group's answers. You can also carry out this exercise as a whole-class activity.

Developing History
Ages 10–11
© A & C BLACK

Finding a builder

- **Imagine you are a Victorian in a new town. Your roof is leaking. How might you find a builder to fix it?**
- **Tick the ways you might use. Explain your choices.**

Look in a street directory ☐

_____

_____

_____

_____

Look on the Internet ☐

_____

_____

_____

_____

Ask a neighbour ☐

_____

_____

_____

_____

Ask the milkman ☐

_____

_____

_____

_____

Look for a builder's yard ☐

_____

_____

_____

_____

Use the Yellow Pages ☐

_____

_____

_____

_____

Now try this!

Imagine your milkman's brother is a builder.
- **Explain how you will contact him.**

Teachers' note Explain to the children what street directories were and how you could use them to find tradesmen. Also explain that milk was delivered door-to-door rather than bought from shops. Do any children have their milk delivered today?

**Developing History
Ages 10–11
© A & C BLACK**

Cleaning up cities

Everyone in the country is sick of commissions and enquiries about their business. The people want to be left alone to manage their own affairs. They do not want parliament interfering in their business.

George Hudson, MP for Sunderland, speaking in 1847, in a parliamentary debate about public health

When cholera breaks out people say 'Nobody is to blame'. What a terrible person Mr Nobody is! He poisons the drinking water and builds streets without drains. He believes people should be left alone. When people are poisoned by bad water, he leaves them alone. When they live in dirty houses, he leaves them alone. He does not interfere with death.

Samuel Smiles, author and editor of the Leeds Times *1838-42, wrote this as part of a report on the debate.*

1. Did Hudson want the government to make laws to clean up cities?

_____

2. What reasons did he give?

_____

_____

3. Did Smiles want the government to make laws to clean up cities?

_____

4. What reasons did he give?

_____

_____

- **Write a speech supporting Hudson or Smiles.**
- **Explain what part of your opponent's view is only their opinion.**

Teachers' note Remind the children of the vocabulary used in the activity on page 13 (the Shaftesbury sheet). Also remind them who Hudson and Smiles are, and make it clear that when Smiles talks of Mr Nobody, he means the government and is being sarcastic.

Developing History
Ages 10–11
© A & C BLACK

Census records: 1

Find out about the past from census returns

1851			1891		
Name	*age*	*Occupation*	*Name*	*age*	*Occupation*
Robert Baxter	43	bootmaker	Fred Dumbletonn	31	bootmaker
Henrietta, wife	41		Alice, wife	31	
William, son	21	bootmaker	Frederick, son	8	
Amy, daughter	20		Ernest, son	5	
John, son	13	apprentice	Percival, son	3	
Frederick, son	13	school	Elinor, daughter	2	
William Tarlton	33	bootmaker	Nathaniel Bennett, father-in-law	77	
Edmund Saw	21	bootmaker			
Michael Husband	21	bootmaker	Lizzie Tew	14	servant
			Annie Green	12	nurse
Thomas Kingerlee	40	builder			
Caroline, wife	43		Alfred Kingerlee	46	draper
William, son	10	school	Charlotte, wife	39	
Thomas, son	8	school	George, son	15	
Alfred, son	6	school	Ann Marks	24	shop assistant
Marianne, daughter	3		Liz Smith	24	shop assistant
			Sarah Smith	19	servant
John Walshaw	48	grocer			
Hannah, wife	52		George Mould	55	photographer
Edward Payne	23	shopman	May, wife	60	
William Page	25	assistant	Henry Bryan	38	hairdresser
Charles Harwell	20	assistant	Marsha, wife	39	
Frederick Sellars	17	apprentice	Charles, son	16	apprentice
John Rattle	17	servant	Florence, daughter	7	
Liz Vause	26	servant	Richard Potter	16	apprentice
Jane York	27	servant	Eliza Blackwell	15	servant
William Potts	51	printer	William Thompson	40	cycle agent
Sarah, mother	81		Enid, wife	35	
William, son	25	reporter	John Potts	60	publisher
John, son	20	apprentice	Sarah, wife	56	
Emma Grissold	20	servant	William, son	22	editor
			Kate, daughter	21	art school
			Bessie, daughter	18	art school
			Fred Speck, brother-in-law	49	soldier

Teachers' note Use this with the activity sheet on page 21.

Developing History
Ages 10–11
© A & C BLACK

20

Census records: 2

Find out about the past from census returns

• **Answer the questions about the census information on sheet 1.**

1. List the different occupations of each head of the household in 1851.

_____

2. List the different occupations of each head of the household in 1891.

_____

3. List any occupations in 1891 connected to new inventions.

_____

4. List the names of any families in both census returns.

_____

5. Do the two census returns show a change in attitudes to children? Explain your answer.

_____

_____

_____

_____

Now try this!

• **Choose one of the large households.**
• **Write a letter from the census-taker to another official describing this household.**

Teachers' note Use this sheet together with the information sheet on page 20. You may prefer to do the exercise as group work or a whole-class activity. Remind the children what the head of the household was then (eldest male) and compare with what it might be now (single mother or guardian).

Developing History
Ages 10–11
© A & C BLACK

Planning a school

Identify characteristic features of Victorian buildings

- **Compare these two plans of Victorian schools.**
- **Write the similarities and differences in the table.**

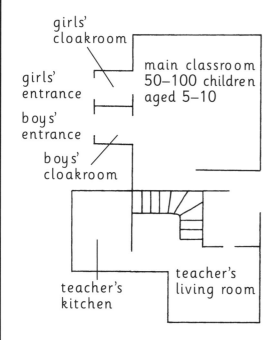

village school

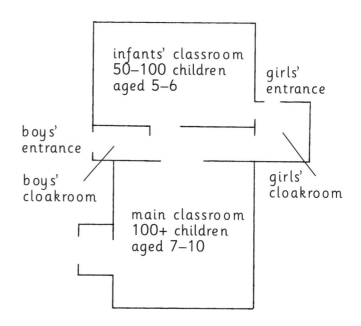

town school

Similarities	Differences

- **Compare these plans with your own school.**
- **Discuss the similarities and differences with a partner.**

- **Choose one of the Victorian school plans.**
- **Draw a picture of the school based on the plan.**

Teachers' note The children should think about the number of classrooms, the school facilities and how the children were split up. There would be children of all ages in each classroom – either all doing the same work or doing different work at the same time in groups. Boys and girls were often separated.

Developing History
Ages 10–11
© A & C BLACK

On the move

Identify characteristic features of Victorian transport and note changes

- **Draw lines to match each type of transport to the purposes it was used for.**

horse cart

walking

horse-drawn bus

canal barge

train

| Visiting relatives | Shop deliveries | Getting to work | Shopping | Factories moving heavy goods |

- **Write why you think each type of transport was used.**

_____

_____

_____

_____

- **Which of these types are still used in your area today?**

_____

_____

Now try this!

- **Using a map of your local area in Victorian times, list the different methods of transport available.**

Teachers' note The children will need a map of your local area in Victorian times for the extension activity. The matching activity could be done as a whole-class activity – with the children suggesting extra uses for transport and transport types. Matches are: Visiting relatives: walk/bus/train; Getting to work: walk/bus/train; Shopping: walk/bus/train; Shop deliveries: horse cart/walk; Factories moving heavy goods: canal/horse cart/train.

Developing History
Ages 10–11
© **A & C BLACK**

Home sweet home

Identify and record characteristic features of a Victorian building

Word bank

sash window
brickwork
Gothic

- **Cut out the pictures. Which is the Victorian house? Glue it onto a sheet of paper.**

- **Label all the Victorian features.**

Now try this!

- **Write a description of the Victorian house for an estate agent. Use as many** adjectives **as you can.**

Teachers' note First make sure the children are familiar with the words in the word bank and with Victorian architecture (see activity notes). Your local library or local council website may have photos of Victorian houses in your area. Once the children have identified the Victorian house, they could compare its features with those on the other three houses. Provide examples of estate agents' property brochures for the extension activity.

**Developing History
Ages 10–11**
© A & C BLACK

Staying in

Understand that the information available depends on the period studied

- **Work with a partner.**
- **Cut out the cards.**
- **Sort the cards into the order the items were invented or made.**

Start with the oldest form of entertainment.

Use an encyclopaedia or the Internet to help you.

television	book	comic	board game

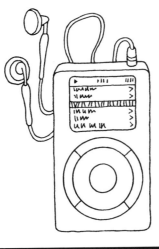

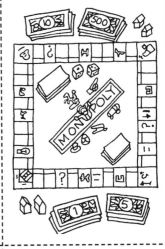

dominoes	mp3 player	cards	radio

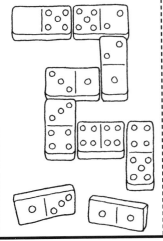

Now try this!

- **Imagine you are being sent back in time to the 1950s.**
- **What one modern piece of equipment would you take with you and why?**

Teachers' note Begin by getting the children to identify the illustrated evidence. Warn the children this exercise is not as easy as it looks. They will need access to information books and/or the Internet. The activity could be adapted to become a whole-class brainstorming activity, or individual/group work with reporting back time at the end. The order of invention is: cards, dominoes, books, board games, radio, comics, television, mp3 player.

Developing History
Ages 10–11
© A & C BLACK

Looking good

- Label each outfit with the decade(s) when it was worn.

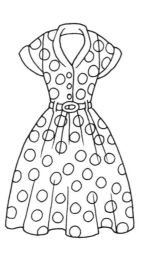

- Choose one of the outfits and write about it.

  What kind of person wore it?

  What does it tell us about that person's life?

_____

_____

_____

_____

_____

_____

Now try this!

- Write a newspaper report from the time the outfit was made. Explain what makes it new and interesting. Give advice about how and when to wear it.

Teachers' note Begin by discussing fashion from the 1940s to the 1990s. If possible, show the children pictures of clothing cut from magazines or printed from the Internet. Point out to them that some of the outfits were worn in more than one decade: long floral dress 1940s/1950s; wide-skirted polka-dot dress 1950s; minidress 1960s; power-suit 1980s/1990s.

Developing History
Ages 10–11
© **A & C BLACK**

Getting the news

There are different ways of getting the world news.

- **For each way, tick the decade (or decades) when it was used.**

Some of the items match more than one decade.

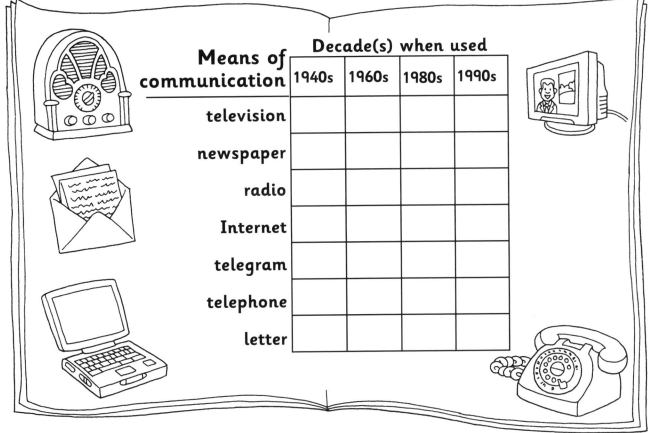

Means of communication	Decade(s) when used			
	1940s	1960s	1980s	1990s
television				
newspaper				
radio				
Internet				
telegram				
telephone				
letter				

- **Work with a partner.**
- **Imagine you live in London in 1950. How would you tell a friend in the USA about your new baby sister?**
- **Write a paragraph explaining how things are different today.**

Now try this!

Imagine you miss the bus home from school.
- **With a partner, discuss what you will do.**
- **What would you have done in 1950?**

Teachers' note Before starting the activity, brainstorm the ways that the children (and adults they know) can pass on news today. Write these on the board.

Developing History
Ages 10–11
© A & C BLACK

Different schools

Distinguish between fact and opinion

Sheila is comparing the school she went to with her grandchild's school.

My school was very different from Clare's. I think mine was better. We sat at desks in rows. The teacher had a desk at the front of the class, by the blackboard. She'd talk to us, maybe put something on the board. Then we had to work in our books. We had to be quiet, no talking. It was nice and quiet. In Clare's school, it is noisy all the time! They talk to each other and move around in lessons. They sit in groups and the teacher goes around the groups. I think it is too noisy. The children seem to like it. I couldn't work like that. But Clare tells me she thinks my school sounds hard to work in!

- **Underline the** | facts | **in blue.**
- **Underline the** | opinions | **in red.**
- **Do you think everyone in Sheila's class would agree with her? Explain your answer.**

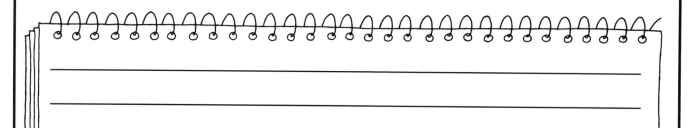

Now try this!

- **Write a report about your school. Make sure it contains no opinions.**
- **List three things that a factual description cannot tell you.**

Teachers' note Remind the children of what they know about Victorian schools. Ask them when they think Sheila, the character on the activity sheet, was at school. It was likely to be in the 1940s, 50s or 60s; invite the children to share what they know about these decades. Revise the difference between facts and opinions, using examples.

Developing History
Ages 10–11
© A & C BLACK

Memories

Understand how personal memories can be used to find out about the past

- **Interview an older relative about their past.**
- **Plan your questions.**
- **Report their answers.**

| Interviewee: | Date: | Time: |

1. When were you born? _____

2. What was your primary school like? _____

_____

_____

3. _____

_____

_____

_____

4. _____

_____

_____

5. _____

_____

_____

- **Work with a partner. Interview each other about your past.**

Teachers' note The children can interview their parents, grandparents or another older relative. Tell them that if they run out of space, they can either use a spare piece of paper or the back of the activity sheet. When they interview each other, they can make an audio recording or write their answers.

Developing History
Ages 10–11
© A & C BLACK

Cause and effect

Identify links and connections between aspects of life in Britain since 1948

• **Match the sentence beginnings and endings.**

A. In the 1950s there were more jobs	**1.** went down.

B. So wages	**2.** making things for the home.

C. This meant people had	**3.** than people to do them.

D. At the same time factories went back to	**4.** went up.

E. They made a lot of goods such as	**5.** bought TVs.

F. TV prices	**6.** cookers, cars and TVs.

G. More people	**7.** more money to spend.

A	
B	
C	
D	
E	
F	
G	

• **Write a paragraph to explain how having more jobs than people to do them led to more people owning TVs.**

_____

_____

_____

_____

_____

• **List a set of causal links for the effects of 25 more children joining your class.**
• **Draw them as a comic strip.**

Teachers' note Make sure that the children understand the idea of causal links before they do the activity. During the plenary, ensure the children have matched up the sentences correctly and talk through any ideas they found difficult to understand, such as why wages go up when there is a shortage of people to do the jobs. The answers are: A3, B4, C7, D2, E6, F1 and G5

Developing History
Ages 10–11
© A & C BLACK

Choosing sources

Compare sources of information available for the study of times in the past

These sources can be used to study pop music in the 1960s.

- **Tick the** primary sources .
- **Explain what you might be able to find out from each source.**

LP recorded in 1969

☐

_____
_____
_____

Book written in 1997

☐

_____
_____
_____

TV show recorded in 1969

☐

_____
_____
_____
_____

Fan magazine printed in 1969

☐

_____
_____
_____

- **List three different primary sources that a person could use to study your life.**

Teachers' note Remind the children of the distinction between primary and secondary sources: primary sources come from the time they are studying, while secondary sources come from a later period. During the plenary, discuss the kinds of information the children can draw from these sources and whether primary sources are necessarily more useful than secondary ones.

Developing History
Ages 10–11
© A & C BLACK

Democracy

Understand what is meant by democracy

- **Read the information about how Greek** city states **were run.**

Greek city states were run in different ways. Many were monarchies: they were ruled by one person. Others were oligarchies: they were ruled by a small group of important people. Athens became a democracy. The word 'democracy' comes from Greek and means 'government by the people'.

In Athens, only men over 18 who were citizens of Athens could vote. Men who were not citizens, along with women, children, slaves and foreigners, could not vote. Less than a third of the people living in the city state could vote. Even so, by 400 BC there were 40,000 voters.

- **Working in groups, discuss this statement.**

Athens was not a democracy.
Not enough people voted.

- **Make notes for a debate.**

- **Use the information about the city states to help you.**

Agree	Disagree

How do you feel about Greek women not being allowed to vote?

Would Greek women have agreed with you?

- **Discuss with a partner.**

Teachers' note Read the information scroll with the children and make sure they understand all the vocabulary. Allow time at the end for them to hold their debate. Each group could take turns while the rest of the class listens.

Developing History
Ages 10–11
© **A & C BLACK**

Don't anger the gods

Learn about the beliefs of the ancient Greeks

The Judgement of Paris

Zeus gave a party for the gods. He did not invite the goddess Eris. She was angry. She threw a golden apple into the party marked 'For the most beautiful one'. The goddesses Athena, Aphrodite and Hera all claimed the apple. They asked Zeus to choose. He didn't want to make trouble, so he said that Paris, the son of the King of Troy (a famous warrior) had to choose.

The goddesses offered different presents to Paris to persuade him to choose them. Paris thought about the different gifts they offered him. He gave the golden apple to Aphrodite. He got what she had offered: the love of the beautiful Helen of Sparta. He took Helen to Troy with him. But King Menelaus, Helen's husband, brought an army to take her away. The war that followed lasted for 10 years. Thousands of warriors were killed, on both sides. Paris was one of them. Menelaus lived and won back his wife.

- **Work in a group. Discuss what the story tells you about ancient Greek beliefs.**

- **Act out the story.**

I'll make you good at fighting and working out tactics.

Athena

I'll make Helen, wife of King Menelaus of Sparta, the most beautiful woman in the world, love you.

I'll make you ruler of all of Asia.

Hera

Paris

'Each goddess spoke to Paris, offering a gift.'

Aphrodite

Now try this!

The Greeks won the Trojan War by a trick.

- **Find out about the story of the Trojan Horse.**

- **Draw a cartoon to summarise the story.**

Teachers' note Discuss with the class that the ancient Greeks told many stories about the adventures of their numerous gods, goddesses, heroes and heroines. We know about these from vase paintings, other artefacts and written sources. Explain that Zeus was the king of the gods. The children can write what the story tells them about ancient Greek beliefs on the back of the sheet. They will need access to books, CD-ROMs or the Internet for the extension activity.

Developing History Ages 10–11 © A & C BLACK

The battle of Salamis: 1

Make inferences about warfare from sources

Source A

In 480 BC, the Persians invaded Greece with a huge army and many ships. They captured several small city states. They beat the Spartan army at Thermopylae. Themistocles, an Athenian, saw a chance to beat the Persians at sea. The Persians had the Greek fleet trapped in a narrow strip of water around the island of Salamis. The Greeks would lose in a fight at sea. But if they could get the Persians to come into the narrow strip of water their ships would be crowded together and easier to attack. Themistocles started a story, which the Persians heard, that the Greeks were planning to escape. When the Greeks seemed to sail away, the Persians chased them. The Greeks waited until the Persians were in the narrow strip of water, then turned and attacked. The Persians lost 200 of their 350 ships. The Greeks only lost 40 of their 310 ships.

A modern historian's account of the battle of Salamis.

Source B

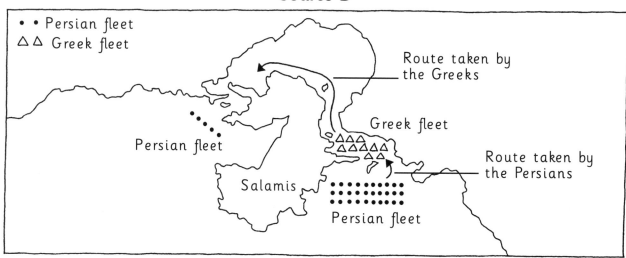

A modern plan of the battle of Salamis.

Source C

The Greeks changed direction as soon as commanded. They came quickly into sight and advanced. You could hear them shout, 'Sons of the Greeks, forward! Free your country, your children, your wives, your temples and the graves of your ancestors! You are fighting for everything!' When the battle was ended the sea was full of wreckage and blood. The beaches and low rocks were covered in corpses. What remained of our fleet were running in terror.

From an English translation of a play written by an ancient Greek playwright. The person speaking is a Persian, bringing the bad news to the Persian king of their defeat at Salamis.

Teachers' note Use this with the activity sheet on page 35.

Developing History
Ages 10–11
© A & C BLACK

34

The battle of Salamis: 2

Make inferences about warfare from sources

• **Answer the questions using the information from sheet 1.**

1. Why did the Greeks want to get the Persians into the narrow strip of water around Salamis?

_____

_____

2. How does Source A support Source B's impression of the battle?

_____

_____

3. What words does the writer of Source C use to suggest the Greeks were well trained and brave?

_____

_____

4. What impression does he give you of the Persians?

_____

_____

5. What impression does he give you of the battle?

_____

_____

_____

6. Is Source C likely to be a biased source? Explain your answer.

_____

_____

_____

Teachers' note Use this sheet together with the information sheet on page 34. Begin with a discussion of sources and recap definitions of primary and secondary sources and bias. The children need to be reminded that the reliability of a source is not any greater just because it comes from the time. Issues that affect reliability affect primary and secondary sources equally.

Developing History
Ages 10–11
© A & C BLACK

Source A

Aren't you scorched by the sun? Aren't you cramped and crowded? Aren't the washing facilities bad? Aren't you soaked to the skin when it rains? Don't you get fed up with all the noise, the shoving and the other annoyances? But I think you are willing to put up with all of this for the marvellous spectacle.

Written by Epictetus (AD 55–135), a Greek thinker, about the Olympic Games.

Source B

Arrachion was fighting another man. The man grabbed him and held him in a tight grip with his legs. With his hands, the man began to strangle Arrachion, who struggled wildly. Finally, Arrachion broke one of his opponent's toes. The opponent gave in, not realising that he had strangled Arrachion to death. Arrachion was named the winner.

From a description of a pankration match, written by a Greek visitor to the Olympics. Pankration was a mixture of wrestling and boxing, with very few rules.

Source C

You must drive your chariot and horses so as to stay as close as possible to the post that marks the point where you turn the corner. Lean right over to the left. Whip the horse on the right, to make him go fast around the turn. At the same time, keep the horse on the left close to the post – so close that the wheel of the chariot seems to touch it. But take care not to even brush the post, or you could crash, harming your horses and breaking the chariot.

Ancient Greek advice about chariot racing, which was one of the events at the Olympic Games.

Teachers' note Use this with the activity sheet on page 37.

Developing History
Ages 10–11
© A & C BLACK

The Olympic Games: 2

Combine information from several sources

- **Read the descriptions of the Greek Olympics on sheet 1.**
- **What does each source tell you about the event?**

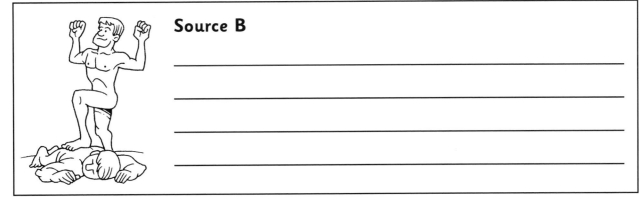

Source A

_____

_____

_____

_____

Source B

_____

_____

_____

_____

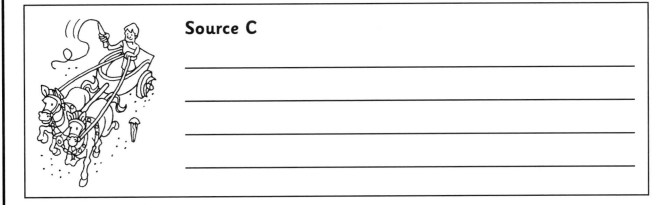

Source C

_____

_____

_____

_____

Now try this!

- **Find pictures of Greek pots showing Olympic events.**
- **Write a paragraph about what they tell you.**
  Think about the pot as well as the picture on it.

Teachers' note Use this sheet together with the information sheet on page 37. You may prefer to do the exercise as group work or a whole-class activity. For the extension activity the children will need access to books or the Internet to find pictures of Greek pots (see resources list on page 8).

Developing History
Ages 10–11
© A & C BLACK

Greek theatre

- **Look at the diagram of a Greek theatre.**
- **Use it to help you complete the chart.**

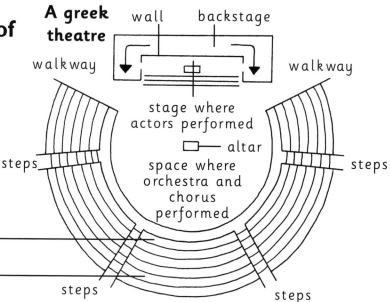

A greek theatre

wall   backstage

walkway   walkway

stage where actors performed

altar

space where orchestra and chorus performed

steps   steps

front row of seats for priests, and important people

up to 15,000 seats for ordinary people

steps   steps

Question	Answer	How you know
Was the theatre just used for plays?		
Which had more members: the orchestra or the group of actors?		
Who went to the theatre?		
What shows that theatres were important?		

- **What would you like to know about Greek theatres that the plan cannot tell you?**

_____

Now try this!

- **Imagine being in the audience at a Greek play.**
- **Write a description of the experience.**

Teachers' note You could have a larger version of the diagram on the board to introduce the activity and for follow-up work. Talk through the various elements of the theatre before the children begin work on the sheet. Remind them of how we know theatrical performances were tied to Greek religious festivals: the altar was for sacrifices, and some seating was labelled for priests.

Developing History
Ages 10–11
© A & C BLACK

Wordy Greeks

Identify suffixes and prefixes of ancient Greek origin

Many English words begin or end with an ancient Greek word, which gives them part of their meaning.

- **What do these ancient Greek beginnings and endings mean? Use a dictionary to help you complete the chart.**

A **prefix** comes at the beginning of a word.

Greek prefix	Meaning	English words with this prefix
auto		
bio		
geo		
micro		
mono		
therm(o)		

Greek suffix	Meaning	English words with this suffix
archy		
gram		
ism		
logy		
meter		
phone		

A **suffix** comes at the end of a word.

Now try this!

- **Find five more Greek suffixes and prefixes in your dictionary. List their meanings.**

Teachers' note Introduce the activity by telling the children that the word 'alphabet' comes from the first two letters of the ancient Greek alphabet, and that many of our words begin or end with a Greek word. Make sure that the children understand the terms 'prefix' and 'suffix'. They will need dictionaries or Internet access for this activity (see resources list on page 8).

Developing History
Ages 10–11
© A & C BLACK

Perfect proportion

Consider the influence of Greek architecture

The Greeks had a mathematical idea about what made a building beautiful. They thought buildings had to be symmetrical and in proportion. The size of parts of the building could change but the proportions remained the same. The proportion they thought most beautiful was a ratio of 9:4. The Parthenon, a huge temple to the goddess Athene, was built to these proportions.

In architecture, a ratio shows the relationship between two measurements.

- **What is the ratio between C and D on the Parthenon diagram? Use the information about Greek buildings to help you.**

  A:B = a ratio of 9:4

  C:D = a ratio of _____

For example, a ratio of 9:4 means that the first measurement is just over twice the length or width of the second measurement.

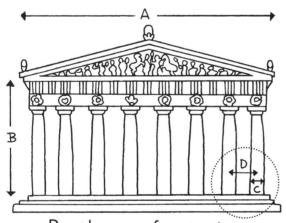

Parthenon front view

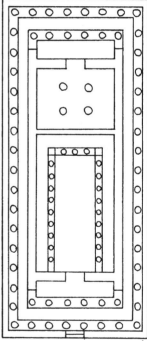

Parthenon floor plan

- **Measure with a ruler and mark three 9:4 ratios on the Parthenon floor plan.**

Now try this!

- **Design a new school building that uses symmetry and proportion.**
- **Show the ratios on your plans.**

Teachers' note Carry out this activity in groups, with a mathematician in each group. Ensure the children understand ratio, symmetry and proportion before starting. The ratio of C, the width of each pillar, and D, the distance between the centre of pillars, is 4:9. On the floor plan, tell the children to mark distances and label them with letters: then show their chosen three as E:F, G:H, I:J. They will need computer access to design a new school building for the extension activity.

Developing History
Ages 10–11
© A & C BLACK

Hippocrates

Appreciate the contribution made by ancient Greek scholars

- **Cut out the cards.**
- **Sort them into the correct order according to the steps Hippocrates followed when treating patients.**

Observe, predict, treat.

If a previous patient displayed these symptoms, check what you did to make them better.	Watch the new patient.	Keep careful records of all symptoms and the treatments given to your new patient.
Meet a new patient.	Ask the patient if they feel different from normal and how.	Treat the patient's symptoms based on your knowledge.
Have you had a patient with these symptoms before? It might help you to predict what to do.	If a previous patient did not display these symptoms, how are the new patient's symptoms different?	

- **A doctor has a patient with totally new symptoms.**
- **Write a note to him from Hippocrates telling him what to do.**

Teachers' note Make sure the children understand medical words such as 'patient', 'treatment' and 'symptoms' before starting the activity.

Developing History
Ages 10–11
© A & C BLACK

Olympic guidebook: 1

Compare the ancient and modern Olympics

- **Fill in the chart comparing the ancient and modern Olympics.**

Question	Ancient Olympics	Modern Olympics
How often did/do they take place?		
Where did/do they take place?		
How long did/do they go on for?		
Number of events: <20 or >20?		
Did/do the athletes wear special clothes?		
Could/can anyone watch the games?		
Where did/do the athletes come from?		
Could/can anyone compete?		
Were/are the games just a sporting event?		

Now try this!

- **Write what you think is the biggest difference between ancient and modern Olympic Games.**
- **Explain your answer.**

Teachers' note The children will need Internet access or books to find out the answers to the questions.

42

Developing History
Ages 10–11
© A & C BLACK

Olympic guidebook: 2

Compare the ancient and modern Olympics

- **Write a time traveller's guidebook entry for the ancient Greek Olympics.**

  Answer all the questions.
  Add more information.

Write your answers on a separate sheet of paper.

What events will I see?

Where will I go? What shall I wear?

Is there anything I must be sure to take?

Is there anything I must be careful not to do?

What sorts of people will be there?

Where will I stay? What's the food like?

Where will the competitors come from?

Now try this!

- **Write what you think the most shocking difference would be for a time traveller.**
- **Explain your answer.**

Teachers' note The children will need a separate sheet of paper for their guidebook entry. Before the children begin the activity, make sure they understand about travel guides – you could bring some in to show them.

Developing History
Ages 10–11
© A & C BLACK

Similar cities

How do the layouts of these Indus Valley cities differ?

- **Make a list on the notepad.**

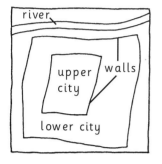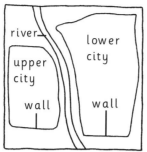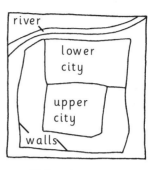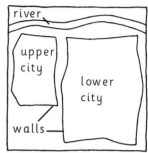

Harappa   Mohenjo Daro   Dholavira   Kalibangan

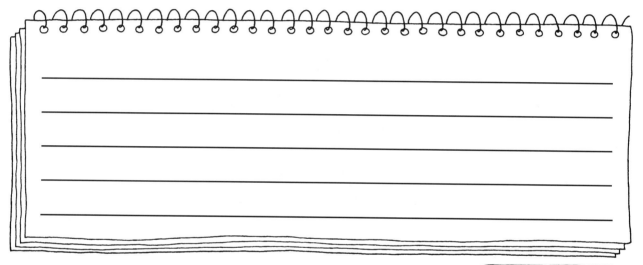

- **How do the shared features suggest the cities were from the same civilisation?**

You can continue your answers on on the back of the sheet.

- **Write a diary entry from the point of view of the archaeologist who drew the plans.**
- **Include what the plans tell you about the people who lived in the cities.**

Now try this!

Teachers' note Introduce the activity by talking about the Indus Valley civilisation, using timelines and maps. Explain that the remains of Indus Valley cities have been excavated by archaeologists to find out about the lives of the people who lived there. Remind the children to think about the similarities between the cities and possible reasons for the differences.

**Developing History
Ages 10–11**

Archaeological evidence

Know the sorts of questions that can be answered from archaeological evidence

- **Read the archaeologists' statements about the remains of a mysterious building found in Mohenjo Daro.**

- **In pairs, discuss what you think it was used for.**

It was a large sunken rectangular area 12 m long and 7 m wide.

It was built with two layers of waterproofed mud bricks with a thick layer of bitumen between them.

There was an open space around the sunken area and a covered walkway.

There was a drain at one end.

It sloped slightly from one end to the other and was 2.4 m at its deepest.

Rooms all around the walkway faced the sunken area.

Pillars pressed the building inwards, so it could stand a lot of pressure from the inside, for example if it was filled with water.

There were steps leading down into the sunken area.

- **Write an article about the building for a history magazine. Explain how the archaeologists' evidence helped you to decide on the building's purpose.**

- **Write a report on the building by an irresponsible journalist. Begin the report:**

The people of Mohenjo Daro all bathed together in a huge bath in the city centre …

Teachers' note First discuss the difference between fact, deduction from evidence and wild speculation. The children should write their reports on a separate sheet of paper. For the extension activity, explain that an irresponsible journalist might draw conclusions that are not sufficiently supported by the evidence.

Developing History
Ages 10–11
© A & C BLACK

Interpreting evidence

Use pictures of artefacts to find out about an aspect of life

- **Work with a partner.**
- **Draw an artefact and label it.**
- **Write what it is made from and what size it is.**

What does the artefact tell you about the people you are studying?

- **List four things on the notepad.**

1. _____
2. _____
3. _____
4. _____

- **Write a description of the artefact for a person who cannot see it.**

Teachers' note The children will need access to photos of artefacts from the period they are studying. They should consider the material the artefact is made from; its purpose; who might have used it; who might have made it and how; whether or not it would have been valuable.

Developing History
Ages 10–11
© A & C BLACK

Different views

Historians are still trying to translate the Indus Valley writing.

- **Answer the questions about the work of these two translators.**

Parpola's translation		Mahadevan's translation	
𑀁	fish or star	𑀁	priest
𑀁	man or servant	𑀁	man or servant
𑀁	cow	𑀁	military officer
𑀁	North Star	𑀁	military officer who acts as priest
𑀁	boy	𑀁	soldier

1. Which symbols appear in both translations?

_____

2. What do the translators agree about?

_____

3. What do the translators disagree about?

_____

4. Who do you think is right?

_____

5. What are the reasons for your answer?

_____

_____

_____

Translating the Indus Valley script is just too hard. The historians should give up.

Do you agree or disagree with this statement?
- **Write a paragraph explaining why.**

Teachers' note Remind the children that no one has fully translated the Indus Valley script yet, so no dictionaries relating to it exist.

Developing History
Ages 10–11
© A & C BLACK

Aztec society

Know about how the Aztec people lived

- **Plan an article for an encyclopaedia about Aztec society.**

- **Create a table about each person's position and job. Include everyone on the diagram.**

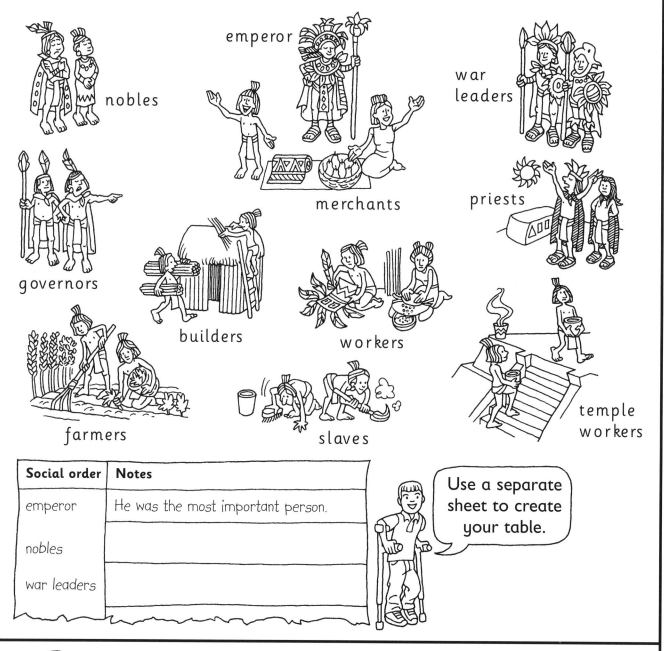

nobles

emperor

war leaders

merchants

priests

governors

builders

workers

farmers

slaves

temple workers

Social order	Notes
emperor	He was the most important person.
nobles	
war leaders	

Use a separate sheet to create your table.

Now try this!

- **Write a description of Aztec society from the point of view of a merchant. Explain how you feel about the people above and below you.**

Teachers' note First show the children detailed encyclopaedia entries and talk about the kind of information they contain. Discuss the hierarchical structure shown in the diagram on the activity sheet and remind the children to think about the rights and duties of each person. The children could go on to write their encyclopaedia entries in groups.

Developing History Ages 10–11
© A & C BLACK

Solve Montezuma's problem

Know that events can be interpreted in different ways

An Aztec legend

The white-skinned god Quetzalcoatl became angry with the Aztecs. He sailed away across the sea, leaving them. He said he would come back, over the sea, from the east. He would bring an army to rule over the Aztecs in peace forever. If they resisted, he would destroy them.

Note: Quetzalcoatl was predicted to return in the year 1519 in the Aztec calendar.

In 1519, Spanish soldiers, led by Cortés, landed on Aztec lands. They brought cannons, guns and horses with them.

- **Work in a group.**

- **Imagine you are the advisers of the Aztec leader, Montezuma. Should you welcome Cortés or put up a fight?**

- **Write notes for a debate on the scales.**

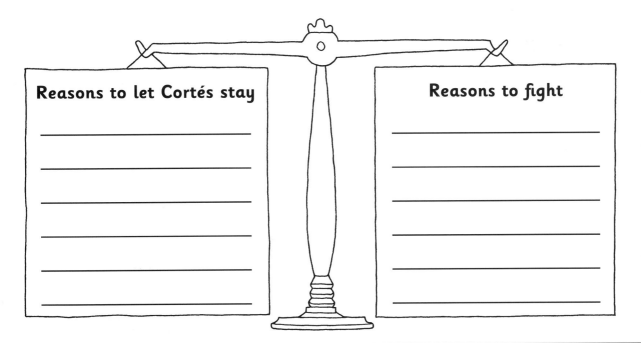

Reasons to let Cortés stay

Reasons to fight

- **Find out what actually happened.**
- **Write a description.**

Teachers' note The children should work in small groups. Tell them they can write on the back of the sheet if they need more space. Once they have made their notes, carry out a whole-class debate and come to a joint decision about the best course of action. For the extension activity the children will need books about the Aztecs or Internet access.

Developing History
Ages 10–11
© A & C BLACK

Reaching conclusions

Know there can be more than one interpretation of the past

- **Complete the chart with the information the children give.**
- **Do you think the Spanish conquest was a good thing?**
- **Discuss with a partner.**

But they made the Aztecs become Catholic and speak Spanish. They destroyed Aztec cities.

The Spanish conquest was a good thing. The Spanish stopped human sacrifice. They taught the Aztecs how to make iron and use the wheel.

The Spanish made the Aztecs slaves. They took all the Aztec gold away to Spain. That's not fair.

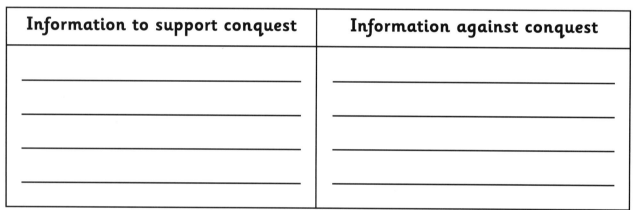

Information to support conquest	Information against conquest
_____	_____
_____	_____
_____	_____
_____	_____

- **Design a badge for each side of the argument for supporters to wear.**

For the Spanish Conquest

Against the Spanish Conquest

Now try this!

- **Write a letter from the king of Spain in 1519 to the governor of Mexico City.**
- **Explain why you want him to make the Aztecs become Catholic and speak Spanish.**

Teachers' note Before the children begin the activity, tell them that all the facts in the speech bubbles are true. Discuss what the children know about the Aztec way of life, and compare this with the way of life of the Spanish invaders, who were Catholics.

Developing History Ages 10–11
© A & C BLACK

Take a closer look

Use pictures to find out about Aztec life

This is a copy of an Aztec picture.

- **With a partner, discuss what the picture tells you about Aztec sacrifice.**

- **Answer the questions.**

1. Write what is happening in the picture.

_____

_____

2. Why did the Aztecs make sacrifices?

_____

_____

3. What does this tell you about their view of the world?

_____

_____

4. Write a short speech for an Aztec, defending sacrifice.

> You can write your speech on the back of this sheet.

- **Write a diary entry by a Spanish soldier after seeing an Aztec sacrifice.**
- **Describe how it made him feel.**

Teachers' note The children should have some prior knowledge of the beliefs and way of life of the Aztecs. Remind the children to think about what is happening in the picture, where and how. For the extension activity, remind the children that a diary is written in the first person and uses the present tense. Link this with work in literacy.

Developing History
Ages 10–11
© A & C BLACK

51

Reasons for exploring: 1

Understand why the Tudors explored outside Europe

Source A

The woods are full of deer, rabbits and large birds. The soil is rich and good for growing crops. The trees are large and better than our oaks. The people there treated us with kindness, and generosity. Beyond this Island called Roanoke, are islands very full of fruits and other crops.

Written by Arthur Barlowe, one of the captains on the first English voyage to Virginia, in 1584.

Source B

The island has trees and plants that give good oil. There are huge grapes, better than grapes from France or Spain. There are many medicinal herbs. There are several kinds of flax. One kind makes a thread like silk. It grows as plentifully as grass does in England. There is plenty of maize to make flour and cane to make sugar. The air is healthy – no one has been sick since we arrived. The savages are very friendly.

From a letter written by Ralph Lane, governor of the Roanoke settlement of 1584, about a week after they landed.

Source C

Reasons for encouraging the settlement of Virginia:

- That this will help to spread the gospel of Christ more widely; something her Majesty is obliged to do.
- That the journey is easy and short and does not cut across the trade routes of any important countries, nor does it cross any of their lands. The journey can be made at all times of the year and needs only one kind of wind. There are plenty of ports on the south and west sides of Ireland which can be used before setting out.
- That her Majesty can charge people trading with this country, once settled, for using her ports on their outward and incoming journeys.
- That it is important to settle new lands quickly, otherwise other countries might take them.
- That these new settlements can be used to search for the Northwest passage to India and China.

From a pamphlet written by Richard Hakluyt, a Tudor explorer, in 1584.

Extra information

- Spices and sugar were very expensive in Europe.
- Silk was very expensive, too.
- The Spanish had found large quantities of gold and silver in South America.
- Many European rulers wanted to take over new lands.

Teachers' note Use this with the activity sheet on page 53.

Developing History
Ages 10–11
© **A & C BLACK**

Reasons for exploring: 2

Understand why the Tudors explored outside Europe

- **Read the sources and the extra information on sheet 1.**

- **List 10 reasons you can find for exploring overseas.**

1. _____
2. _____
3. _____
4. _____
5. _____
6. _____
7. _____
8. _____
9. _____
10. _____

- **List 5 more reasons why the Tudors might have gone exploring.**

_____
_____
_____
_____
_____

- **Make a poster to encourage people to settle in Virginia.**
- **Sketch it first, to plan where things will go.**
- **Produce it on paper or on a computer.**

Teachers' note Tell the children they can write their explanations for the second part of the activity on the back of the sheet. Read the sources and the additional information as a class, working through any difficult vocabulary. Explain that the word 'savage' was used then to describe a person who has not been brought up as a Christian and was not necessarily rude in the way it is today. Remind the children that travelling overseas in Tudor times was uncomfortable and dangerous.

Developing History
Ages 10–11
© A & C BLACK

Cross the Atlantic

Appreciate the discomforts of exploration

- **Play the game in pairs.**
- **Roll a six to start the game.**

Anchors take you down, rigging takes you up, scrolls have special instructions.

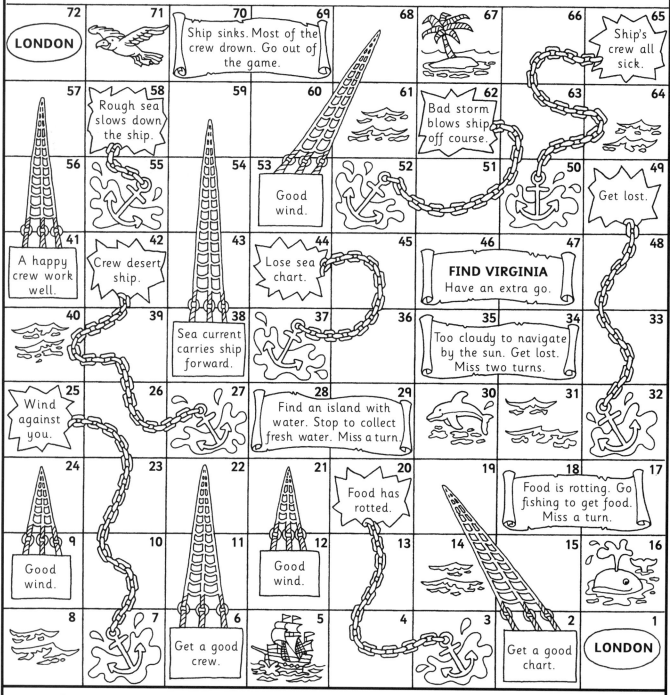

- **Make a list of disasters you had.**
- **Compare your journey with your partner's.**

Now try this!

Teachers' note Each pair of children needs one copy of the sheet, two counters and a dice. Explain that the game is based on snakes and ladders and they should take it in turns to roll the dice and move their counter. The winner is the first to complete the voyage and make it back to London (square 72). The children could make a pencil mark on the instruction squares they land on, to use in the extension activity.

Developing History Ages 10–11
© **A & C BLACK**

The people of Virginia

Find out about the way of life of the indigenous people before colonisation

The village of Secotan, drawn by John White, one of the English explorers in 1585.

- **What does the picture tell you about the people living in Secotan village in Virginia?**

_____
_____
_____
_____
_____
_____

Now try this!

- **Write a description of the houses in Secotan.**
- **Would you have liked to live in one?**
- **Explain your answer.**

note Explain to the children that Roanoke Island in Virginia, where Secotan village existed, was the first place America where the English tried to settle. Show them the location of Roanoke Island on a map. Tell the children ntinue their answer on the back of the sheet.

Developing History
Ages 10–11
© A & C BLACK

Things go wrong

Settlers arrived in Roanoke in 1584 and 1585.

At first they were happy, but then things went wrong.

- **Working in groups, discuss reasons for staying or going home.**

- **Carry out a vote to make a decision.**

> We should have planted food and learned to fish as soon as we arrived. Then we would not have needed to take the savages' food.

> We are soldiers and miners, not farmers. We were told to build a fort and look for gold and pearls. So we did. They should have sent some farmers too.

> The savages were friendly at first. Taking their food and burning their villages made them angry. Then Ralph Lane killed their king. No wonder they hate us and won't help us anymore.

> The ships with more food haven't come from England. Sir Frances Drake has stopped here on his way back to England from the West Indies. He has offered us a ship to go home. We should take it.

- **List the reasons for the group's decision.**

_____

_____

_____

_____

_____

Now try this!

- **Write a paragraph explaining what went wrong.**
- **How might this have caused problems for future settlers?**

Teachers' note You could have a larger version of the diagram on the board for follow-up work. Introduce the activity by saying that, following the first expedition in 1584, an expedition was sent in 1585. It was led by Ralph Lane. At first, things went well (he wrote the letter that is Source B on page 52). Then things began to go wrong, as the speech bubbles explain.

Developi
Year 6
© A & C

Understand why the Roanoke settlement failed

John White's story

I was on the 1585 expedition to Virginia. I thought we could settle there, but it ended badly. Bad decisions were made and we fought with the local people. In 1587 I was asked to be governor of the next settlement. I was glad there were families and farmers, not just soldiers. I was also glad we were to settle in nearby Chesapeake Bay, not Roanoke. The local people would be less hostile. My pregnant daughter Eleanor and her husband came as settlers.

We arrived in late July and anchored near Roanoke. I went to find the 15 soldiers we had left behind in 1586. The fort was empty, except for one dead body. Everyone else had vanished. Simon Fernandez, our captain, refused to go to Chesapeake Bay. He said he had to set off for England, before the weather got too bad for him to sail safely. So the settlers had to get off in Roanoke. I had to leave with Fernandez to get more supplies to bring back in the spring.

Before we set off, my daughter had her baby, a little girl called Virginia. It was hard to leave them behind. When we got to England it was impossible to return as soon as I wanted. There was trouble with Spain. All English ships were needed to fight the Spanish. We did not get back to Roanoke until August 1589. The settlers had built homes and a fence around the town and farmed some land. But everyone had vanished. There were no bodies. The settlement and fort had been broken into and robbed. The only clue was the name of an island, Croatoan, carved on a fence post. We tried to get there, but the weather was bad. We were running out of supplies and time to get back to England in good weather. We waited several days, but the weather did not improve. The captain decided to go back to England.

ote Use this with the activity on page 58.

Developing History
Ages 10–11
© A & C BLACK

Lost: 2

Understand why the Roanoke settlement failed

There are several historical theories about what happened to the Roanoke settlers. Each theory has its own problems.

- **Which theory do you agree with?**
- **Explain what you think happened and why.**
- **Write your answers on a separate sheet.**

Theory 1: **The local people made them slaves or killed them.**

Problems: The local people did not have slaves.
If they killed them it was not at the settlement, but somewhere else.

Theory 2: They died from disease.

Problems: Why were there no bodies in the settlement, or a big burial place outside?

Theory 3: They went to live with the local people.

Problems: Would the local people have accepted them?

Theory 4: They went to live somewhere else.

Problems: They could have gone to Croatoan or another part of the mainland but no one has found any sign of settlement on Croatoan from the time.
Did they go to Chesapeake as they had intended?

Now try this!

- **Write a paragraph describing how you think John White felt when he could not reach Croatoan.**

- **What do you think he said to his family when he got home?**

Write on the back of the sheet.

Teachers' note Use this sheet together with the information sheet on page 57. It will be helpful if the children have first completed the activity on page 56. Read the information sheet to the class before the children begin the activity. This is a good exercise for individual work. The children's ideas can be collated on the board during the plenary.

Develo
Ages
© A

Changing our lives

Show the impact of Tudor exploration on life today

- **Circle the things that the Tudor explorers discovered.**

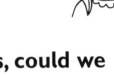

Use books, CD-ROMs or the Internet to find out.

If the Tudors had not discovered these things, could we still have them today?

- **Explain how it might be possible.**

_____

_____

_____

_____

_____

_____

_____

_____

Now try this!

Were the Tudors wrong to bring back tobacco and say it was good for you?

- **List your reasons.**

Note The children will need access to books, CD-ROMs and the Internet for this activity. Tell the children to ...efully about their choices.

Developing History
Ages 10–11
© A & C BLACK

Mary Quant

Research the basic details of a person's life and present them chronologically

- **Plan a profile for a TV programme about Mary Quant's life.**
- **Use books, CD-ROMs and the Internet to find out about her.**
- **Make notes on the chart.**

MARY QUANT: A LIFE IN FASHION for Channel 9	
Born:	**Education:**
Her first shop	
The mini skirt	
Famous friends	
Awards	
Personal life	
Other facts	

- **Make a timeline of Mary Quant's life.**
- **Underline the three events you think were the most significant.**
- **Write a sentence for each one to explain why.**

Teachers' note The children will need access to books, CD-ROMs and the Internet for this activity. First discuss what kind of information would be included in a television documentary about the life of someone famous, and read through the headings on the chart with the class. The children could role-play interviewing Mary Quant once they have completed the activity.

Develo
Ages
© A

The swinging sixties

Consider some reasons for the fashion changes of the sixties

In the mid-1960s London became known as 'Swinging London' for the way it seemed to be leading changes in music and fashion.

- **Read what Joan Shuter, a 43-year-old post office worker at the time, says about the changes.**

During the war clothes were rationed. I was 23 when the war ended. I was sick of mending clothes! After the war there was more choice of clothes and new fashions, made with lots of fabric. It was wonderful. In the mid-1960s people began making clothes for teenagers – clothes that women of my age couldn't wear. We would have looked silly in long white plastic boots or really short skirts. There hadn't really been teenage fashion before. These clothes were badly made, to be cheap enough for teenagers to buy them. I was used to clothes that lasted for years and years. I didn't like them.

- **List two ways that fashion changed between the end of the war and the mid-1960s according to Joan.**

    1. _____

    2. _____

- **Think of a reason for each change.**

    1. _____

    2. _____

- **Write on a separate sheet how a teenager would have felt about the new clothes.**

Now try this!

- **Write a letter from Joan to her sister, explaining why she dislikes the new fashions.**

Discuss with children the concept of the 'generation gap' and how adults' and teenagers' opinions at this greatly divided.

Making minis fashionable

• **Join the correct parts of the sentences together.**

John Bates designed the first mini	in 1965, and sold them cheaply.
The French designer, Courrèges, made minis popular	in 1964, but they were expensive.
Mary Quant opened her own shop to sell minis she designed herself	in 1963, but shops refused to sell it.

Who do you think should get the credit for inventing the mini?

• **Underline the point of view you most agree with.**

Some people think Bates should get the credit for the mini. He designed the miniskirt before Mary Quant or Courrèges.

Courrèges was the first person to make people notice the mini on the catwalk. Bates couldn't get people to accept the mini. Courrèges did.

Mary Quant made minis popular. She sold them cheaply enough so that everyone could buy one. Courrèges' minis were far too expensive so what use were they? She should have the credit.

• **Explain your choice to a partner.**

• **Write a chant supporting Bates, Mary Quant or Courrèges.**

Teachers' note Remind the children that making judgements is often subjective and depends on the criteria you use to make the judgement.

Devel
Ages
© A

62

Fashion plus: 1

Begin to evaluate the impact of an individual on the history of their time

Source A

The 1960s was the first decade when all young women stayed at school until 16 and went to university in large numbers. The image of women changed from a wife and mother to a young, free, single girl. And the miniskirt seemed to express it all. Mary Quant made ready-to-wear, affordable clothes for the new image. The miniskirt was a symbol of the new freedom of young women. Single, working, women could choose (and pay for) their own clothes.

From 'Looking Good, Feeling Free!', written by Tom Robbins, in the New York Times *in 1995.*

Source B

When I went to art college there was nothing for young people. The older generation wanted to get back to the way we lived before the war. We wanted to go forward, do something new. The art schools were full of talented people and they wanted to change everything: music, design, food, furnishing and even politics. When we set up Bazaar in 1955, we hung out around the King's Road coffee bars. People called us 'the Chelsea Set' and we were the focus for people who wanted change.

From Quant by Quant, *Mary Quant's autobiography.*

Source C

It was just fashion. Minis were shocking to some people at the time, but I don't think that means that Mary Quant was important or part of an important change. The important changes were the way that ordinary people started to join together to oppose government decisions. The CND campaigned against nuclear weapons. It was an important change. It was started in 1958 and I joined after hearing about their first big march.

From an interview with Ivy Gross, who lived in Devon during the 1960s.

Read the sources with the class. Point out that source A is a secondary source, sources B and C are ... they were written by people about times they lived through. Check that the children understand ... ns are and explain that CND stands for the Campaign for Nuclear Disarmament. Use this with the ... 64.

Fashion plus: 2

Begin to evaluate the impact of an individual on the history of their time

- **Complete the chart using the sources from sheet 1.**
- **Explain your answers.**

Question	Source A	Source B	Source C
Is this a primary or secondary source for studying 1960s fashion?			
Does the source support the idea of the importance of fashion or not?			

- **Which source do you agree with most?**
- **Make notes for a speech defending your choice.**

- **Prepare a blog for the Internet about how you would like to have an impact on the history of your time.**

Teachers' note Use this sheet together with the information sheet on page 63. You may prefer to do the exercise as group work or a whole-class activity. Remind the children of the distinction between primary and secondary sources. Allow time at the end of the activity or in another lesson for the children to give their speeches.